Turtle Flies South

There once lived a very talkative turtle. He had a smooth, thick shell, and he was very proud of it. "Look," he would say to the other animals, "see how my shell protects me from harm. You don't have a shell like mine!"

Turtle was always talking
about the things he'd like to do.
"You're all so boring!" he said.
"You never do anything interesting!
Why, if I had the chance,
I'd love to travel the world."
He went on and on until all the
animals were tired of listening.

zzzzz

3

One day, when leaves were falling, and a cool wind was blowing, Turtle noticed a flock of birds gathering in the trees. What a noise they made!

"Hey!" said Turtle. "What's going on?"

"It will be winter soon," said the birds.
"We're getting ready to fly south, where
it's warm and there's plenty of food."

5

Turtle was very interested when he heard this.

"Can I come with you?" he asked. "I've always wanted to travel!"

"Don't be silly! You're a turtle!" said the
birds. "Turtles can't fly!"

"There must be some way you could
take me," he said. He begged and pleaded,
until the birds agreed to take him along
with them.

"Can you hold this stick with your mouth?" said one.

"Of course I can! Once I grab something, nothing can make me let go," said Turtle.

So he grabbed the stick with his mouth,
and the two biggest birds flew into the air,
holding the stick between them.

"But remember," said one of the other
birds, "you must not open your mouth
until we get there."

Turtle liked being up in the sky. He felt that he was finally on the way to adventure.

It was fun to look down from the clouds and see how small everything seemed.

But soon he began to wonder how much farther it was to the south.

He had lots of questions that he wanted to ask – but he remembered that he had to keep his mouth shut.

Turtle tried signaling to the birds. First, he rolled his eyes, but the birds didn't even notice. Then he tried waving his legs, but the birds just kept on flying.

"Mmmph!" he said, as loudly as he could with his mouth shut. But that still didn't work.

Finally, he became so angry that he lost his temper and shouted, "Why...aaaagh!" But that was all he said.

Down and down and down he fell.

He pulled his legs and his head inside his shell and closed his eyes tightly.

Thud!

He hit the ground, and his thick, smooth shell cracked all over.

Turtle was very unhappy. He decided
he'd seen enough of the world to last
him a lifetime.

He crawled away to the nearest pond and
dug himself into the mud at the bottom.
Then he fell asleep.

Ever since the time of that foolish turtle, turtles sleep all through the winter.

They know when to keep their mouths shut, too. And they no longer have smooth shells!